Also by Don Martin

MAD'S MADDEST ARTIST DON MARTIN BOUNCES BACK!

Drawn by Don Martin

Written by Don Martin and E. Solomon Rosenblum

A SIGNET BOOK

Published by the New American Library, New York and Toronto
The New English Library Limited, London

N·A·L
SiGNET
BOOKS

SIGNET BOOKS are published *in the United States* by
The New American Library, Inc.,
1301 Avenue of the Americas, New York, New York 10019,
in Canada by The New American Library of Canada Limited,
295 King Street East, Toronto 2, Canada,
in the United Kingdom by The New English Library Limited,
Barnard's Inn, Holborn, London, E. C. 1, England

PRINTED IN THE UNITED STATES OF AMERICA

FESTER AND KARBUNKLE

IN

NATIONAL GORILLA-SUIT DAY

WHAT ARE YOU DOING IN THAT STUPID COSTUME, YOU MORON?!! HAVEN'T YOU HEARD ONE WORD I'VE SAID?!!? AREN'T YOU SUPPOSED TO BE A FRIEND OF MINE?!!?!!

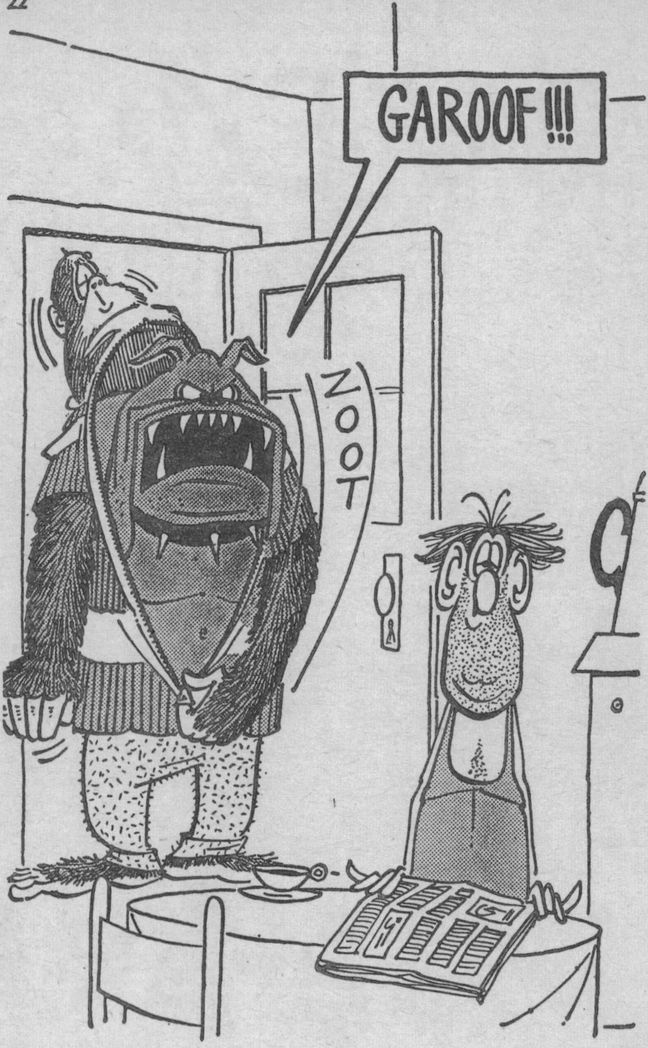
GAROOF!!!
ZOOT

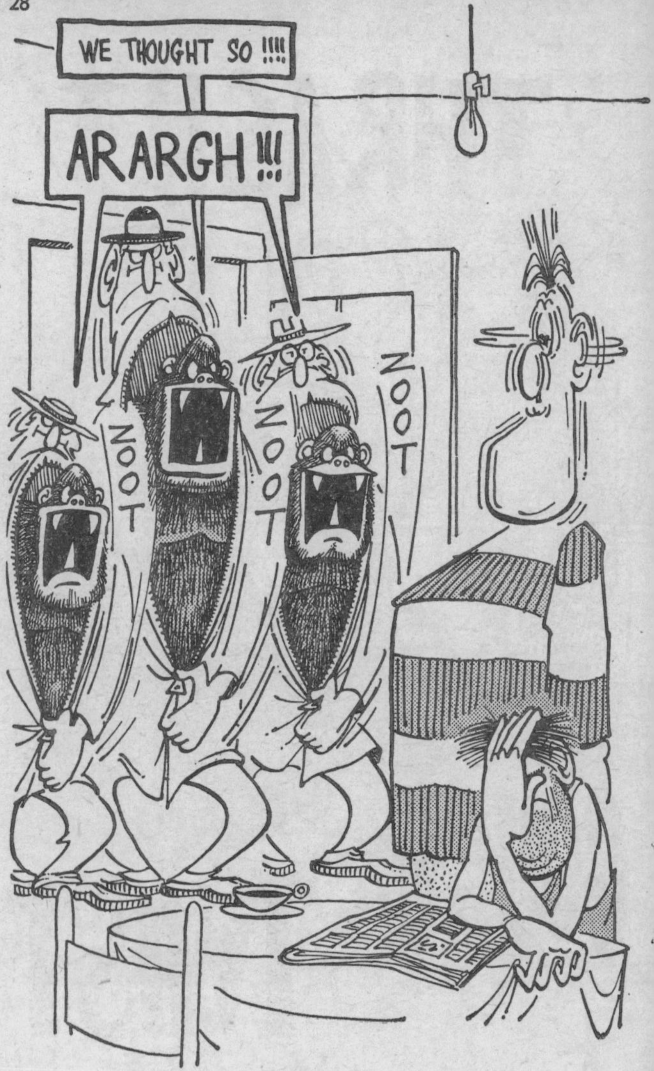
WE THOUGHT SO !!!!
ARARGH !!!
NOOT
NOOT
NOOT

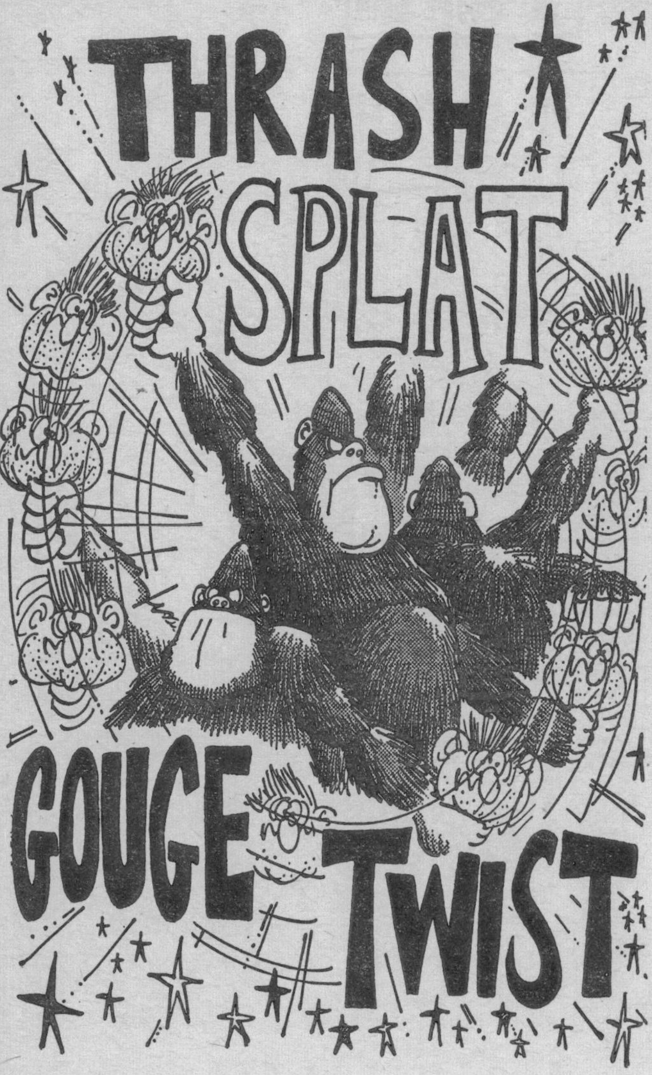
THRASH
SPLAT
GOUGE
TWIST

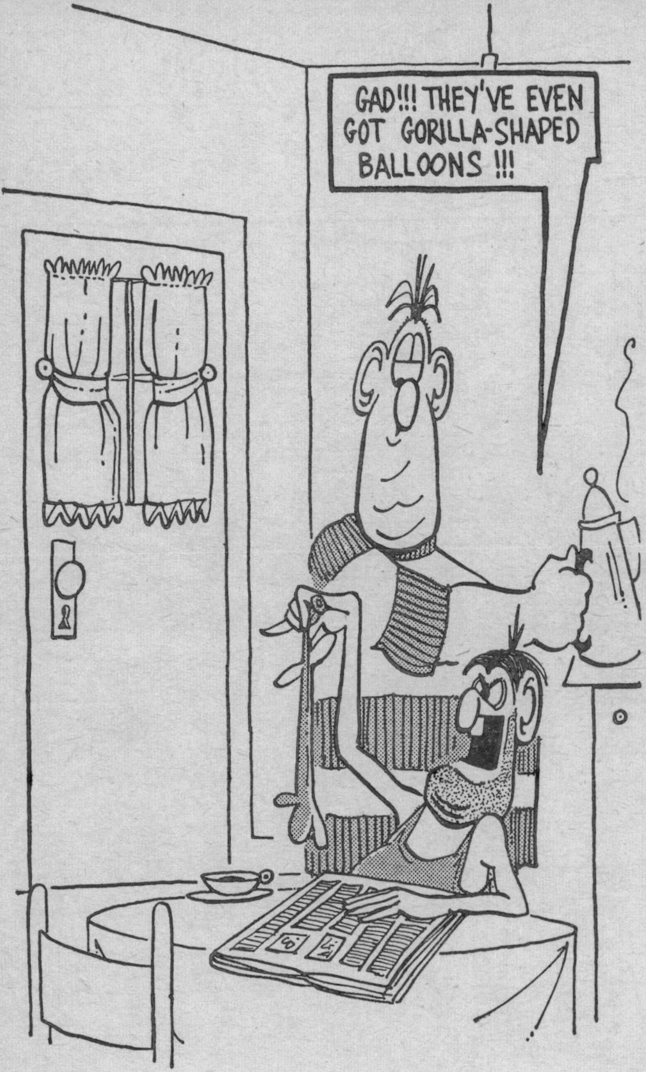
GAD!!! THEY'VE EVEN GOT GORILLA-SHAPED BALLOONS !!!

BY GOLLY, KARBUNKLE !! IT WORKS !!! BY SIMPLY LOOKING AT THIS DIAL I CAN SEE THAT IT'S NOT SOMETHING IN SOME KIND OF SUIT, BUT THAT IT'S A REAL LIVE FLESH-AND-BLOOD GORILLA !!!
ARARGH !!!

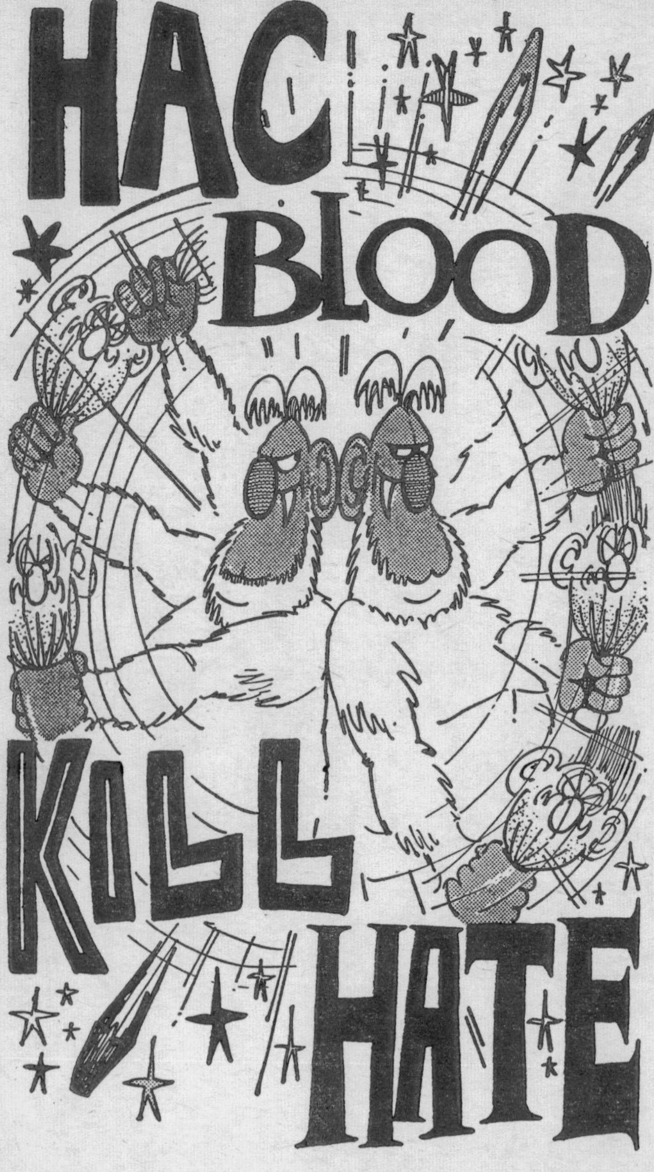
HAC
BLOOD
KILL
HATE

FESTER BESTERTESTER

in

A Visit To The Dentist

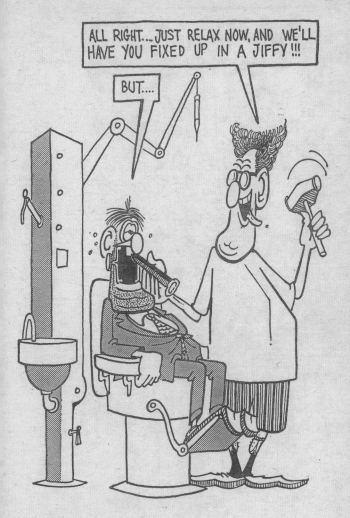

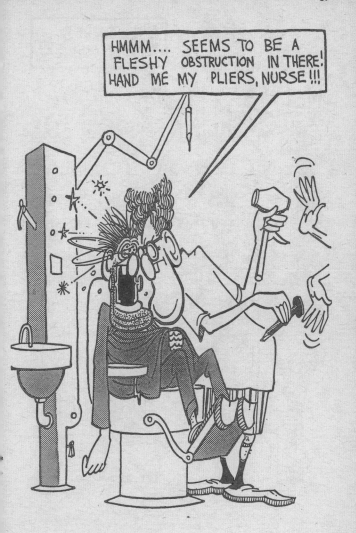

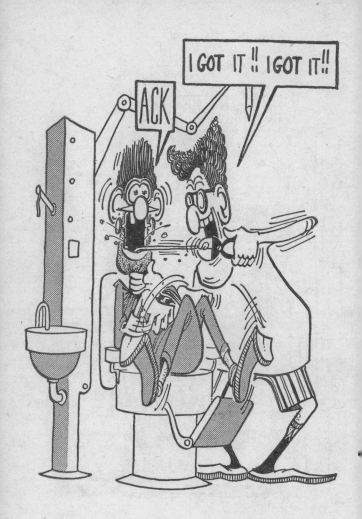

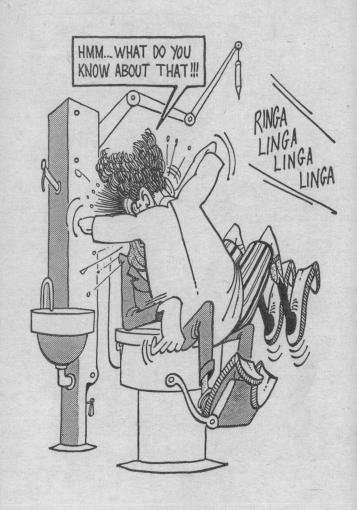

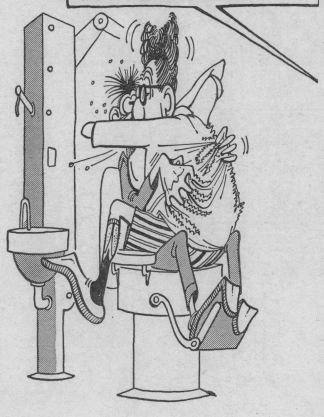

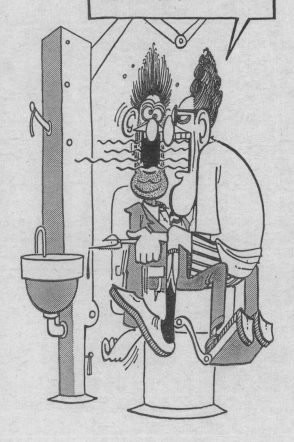

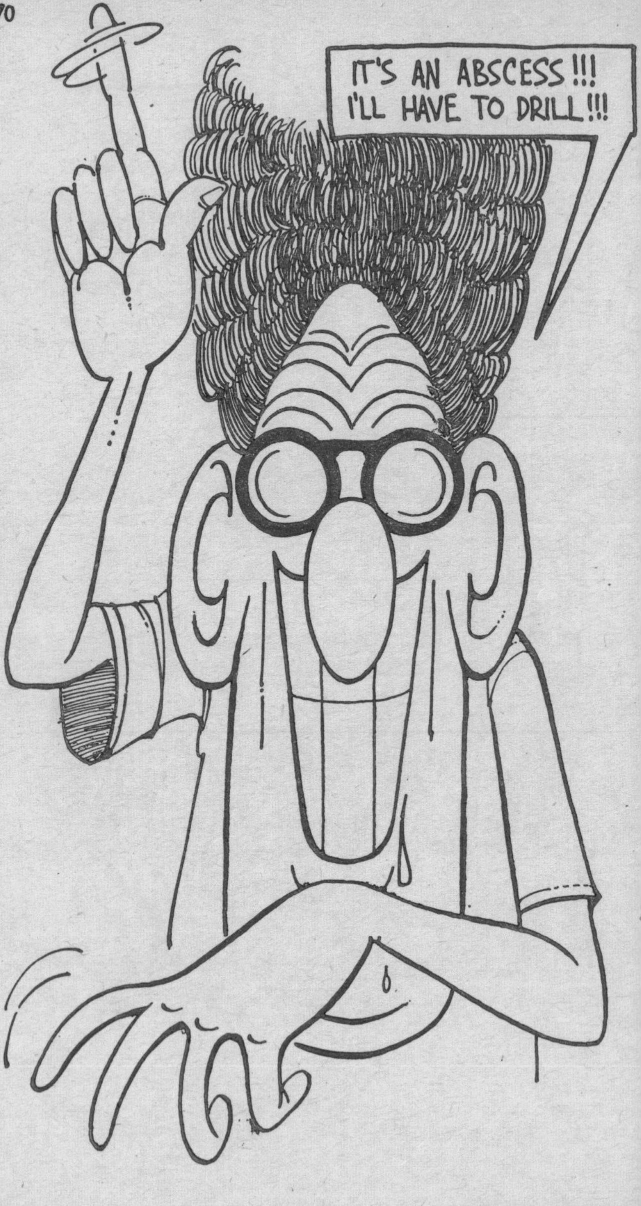
IT'S AN ABSCESS!!!
I'LL HAVE TO DRILL!!!

STEADY NOW, HERE SHE COMES....AND REMEMBER!! IT'S NOT THE PAIN.... ONLY THE PRESSURE OF THE DRILL UPON THE EXPOSED NERVE !!
HUMMMMMM

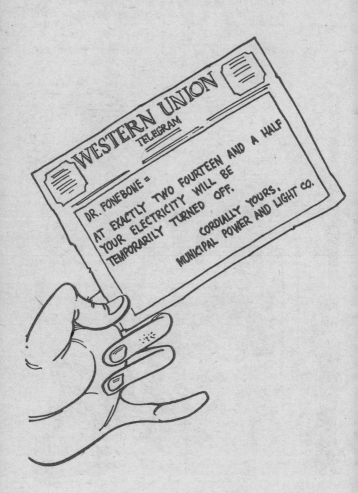

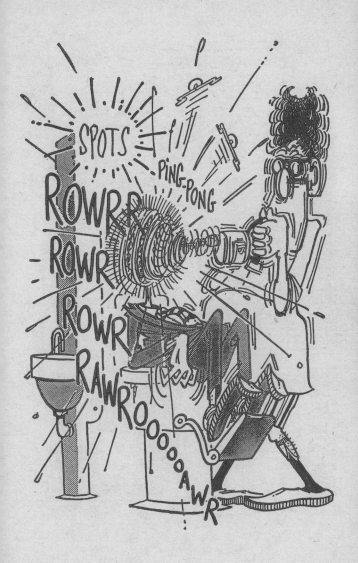

FESTER AND KARBUNKLE

IN

THE HARDEST HEAD IN THE WORLD

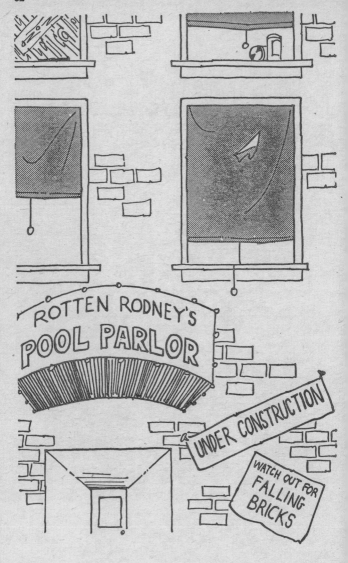

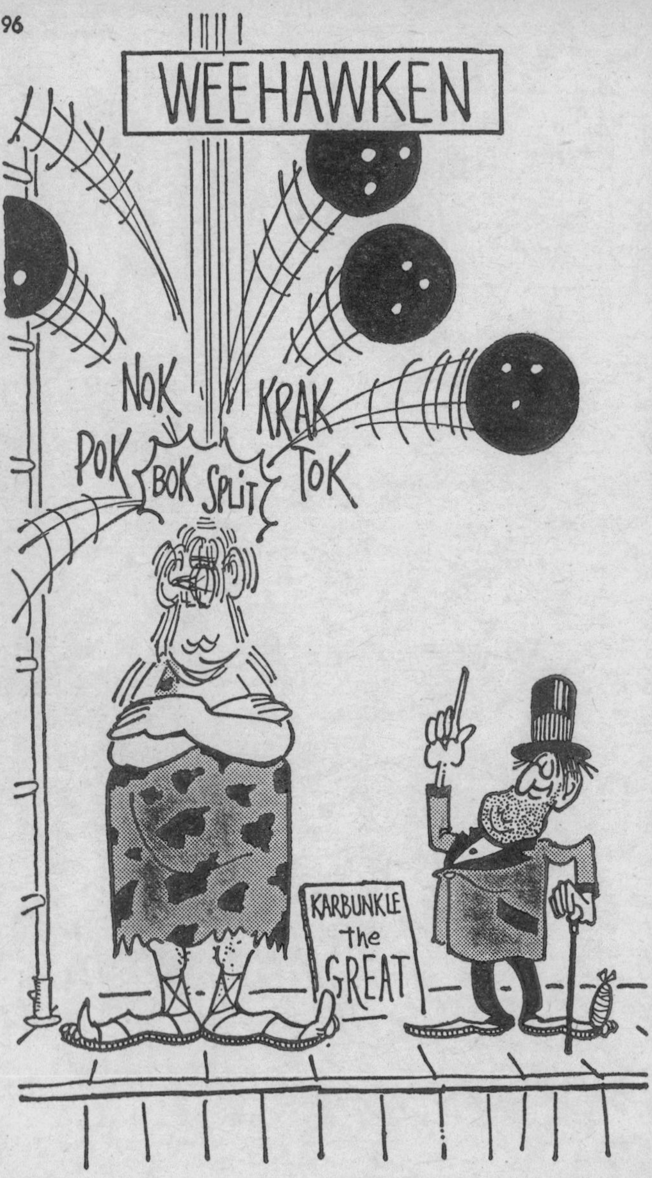
WEEHAWKEN
NOK
KRAK
POK
BOK
SPLIT
TOK
KARBUNKLE the GREAT

NEW
YORK

GAAH!

AND SO IT CAME TO PASS
THAT TWO AMERICAN BOYS
EMERGED FROM HUMBLE BEGIN-
NINGS TO CARVE OUT FOR
THEMSELVES A CAREER THAT
WAS DESTINED TO MAKE THEM
STAND AS A CREDIT TO THEIR
RACE.... LET US NOW FOL-
LOW FESTER AND KARBUNKLE
AS THEY RIDE THE CREST
FROM POVERTY TO RICHES...
FROM OBSCURITY TO FAME...
FROM THE STREETS TO THE
PENTHOUSE....

THAT NIGHT

TWO-TON
STEEL
GIRDER

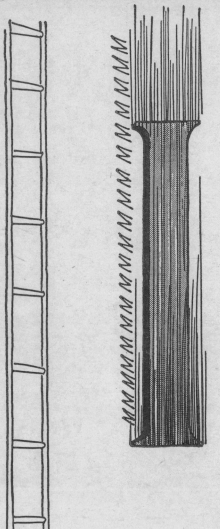

HEAD

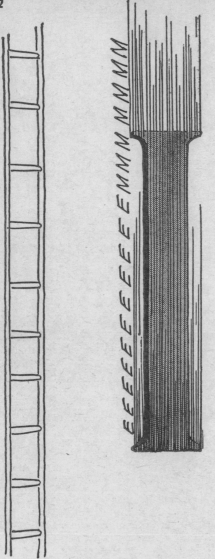

OSHKOSH

128

SKID ROW GULCH

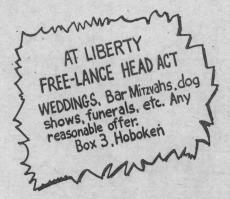

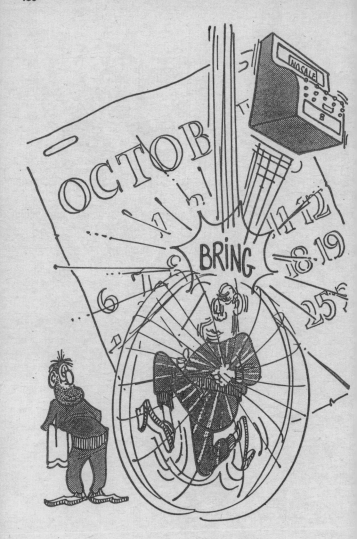

IT'S A GREAT DAY HERE ON THE EGYPTIAN DESERT, LADIES AND GENTLEMEN.... THE SUN IS SHINING.. THE CROWD IS ENTHUSIASTIC...AND IN JUST A FEW MINUTES WE WILL WITNESS THE MOST DARING FEAT IN HISTORY.....

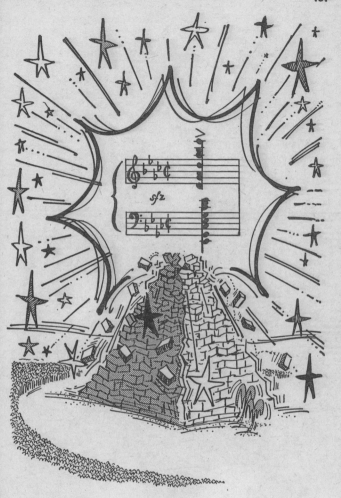

FESTER AND KARBUNKLE

IN

SWAN LAKE

IT IS NIGHT.... PRINCE SIEGFRIED, DISGUISED IN A SATYR SUIT, IS CAVORTING IN A SMALL GLADE NEAR THE LAKE.

SUDDENLY, HE IS STARTLED BY THE SOUND OF
FLUTTERING WINGS, AND HASTENS TO CONCEAL
HIMSELF.

NO SOONER HAS SIEGFRIED HIDDEN THAN THE
MOST BEAUTIFUL WOMAN HE HAS EVER SEEN
ENTERS THE QUIET GLADE.....

HE CANNOT BELIEVE HIS EYES, FOR THE
MAGNIFICENT CREATURE APPEARS TO BE BOTH
SWAN AND MAIDEN....

SHE TELLS SIEGFRIED SHE IS ODETTE, QUEEN OF
THE SWANS....THAT SHE AND THE OTHER SWAN
MAIDENS WERE TURNED INTO BIRDS BY AN
EVIL SORCERER NAMED VON FONEBONE.

...THAT SHE ASSUMES HUMAN FORM ONLY BETWEEN MIDNIGHT AND DAWN-AND THUS IT WILL BE UNTIL A MAN LOVES HER, MARRIES HER, AND NEVER LOVES ANOTHER.

SIEGFRIED SAYS **HE** WILL LOVE HER, MARRY HER, AND NEVER LOVE ANOTHER, AND ODETTE DOES A GRACEFUL PA-DA-TWEE INTO HIS WAITING ARMS.

VON FONEBONE, WHO HAS BEEN HOVERING OVER-
HEAD DISGUISED AS AN OWL, DESCENDS ON THE
SCENE AND DEMANDS THAT ODETTE RETURN TO HIM.

SHE REACHES OUT DESPERATELY FOR SIEGFRIED,
BUT UNDER THE SPELL OF VON FONEBONE, SHE
IS CARRIED HELPLESSLY AWAY.

SIEGFRIED, MOTIONLESS IN HIS GRIEF FOR A MOMENT, SUDDENLY LIFTS HIS HEAD TO THE HEAVENS AND SWEARS HIS INFINITE LOVE.

VON FONEBONE'S SPELL IS BROKEN BY THE
STRENGTH OF SIEGFRIED'S PASSION, AND
ODETTE IS RELEASED.

TRUE LOVE FINALLY TRIUMPHS IN THE END,
AND VON FONEBONE WITHERS AND DIES.

AND WITH THE FINAL NOTE OF MUSIC, WE SEE
ODETTE BEND LOW TO HER LOVER AND GIVE
HIM THE BLESSED TOKEN OF HER
UNDYING LOVE.

♪ CURTAIN ♪

FESTER BESTERTESTER

AS

THE

BARBER

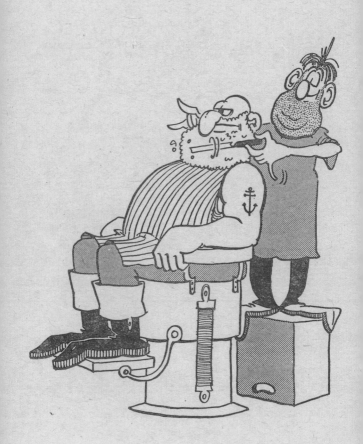

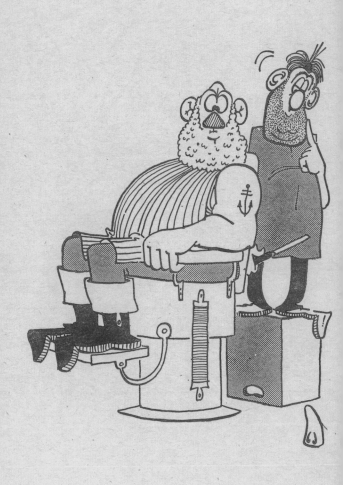

FESTER AND KARBUNKLE

in

THE

GOURMET

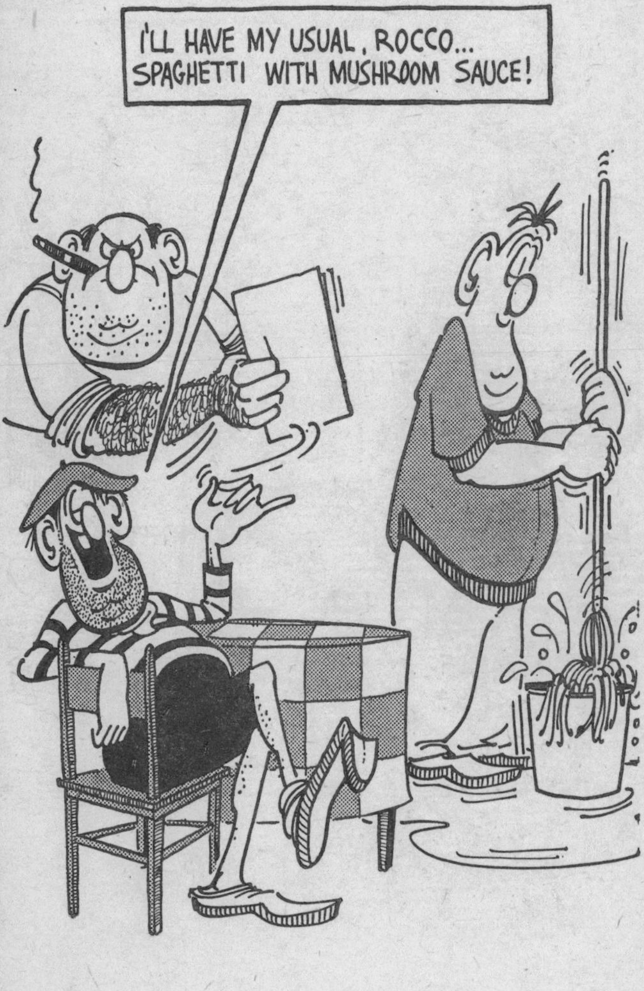
I'LL HAVE MY USUAL, ROCCO...
SPAGHETTI WITH MUSHROOM SAUCE!

FESTER AND KARBUNKLE

IN

THE PAINTERS

GLURGLE
LURGLE
LURGLE
LURGLE
LURGLE